This is the story of ordinary people confronting the extraordinary.

On a moonlit night near Muncie, Indiana, two strangers witness the inexplicable—unidentified flying objects in the sky above them. From that moment on, their lives are irrevocably entwined and forever changed.

Their desperate efforts to understand what they have experienced tears them away from the life they knew, plunges them into the world of governmental cover-ups and intrigue and draws them to the one place that will hold the answers to the ultimate encounter.

◆

A MANDALA PRODUCTIONS FOTONOVEL™

CLOSE ENCOUNTERS
OF THE THIRD KIND

based on the screenplay by
STEVEN SPIELBERG

A DELL BOOK

CLOSE ENCOUNTERS OF THE THIRD KIND

Published by
Dell Publishing Co., Inc.
1 Dag Hammarskjold Plaza
New York, New York 10017

Dell® TM 681510, Dell Publishing Co., Inc.

ISBN: 0-440-10979-5

Printed in the United States of America

First printing—March 1978

Designed by
Michael Parish, Los Angeles

A Columbia / EMI Presentation

CLOSE ENCOUNTERS
OF THE THIRD KIND

A Phillips Production   A Steven Spielberg Film

starring
RICHARD DREYFUSS

also starring

TERI GARR   MELINDA DILLON

with
FRANÇOIS TRUFFAUT
as Lacombe

music by   JOHN WILLIAMS
visual effects by   DOUGLAS TRUMBULL
director of photography   VILMOS ZSIGMOND, A.S.C.

produced by
JULIA PHILLIPS and MICHAEL PHILLIPS

written and directed by
STEVEN SPIELBERG

AN INTERVIEW WITH
P.J. WILLCOX

by MR. PAT QUIGLE

In 1969, after over twenty years of near continuous effort, the United States Air Force stopped all investigations of Unidentified Flying Objects (UFOs). This decision was based on a recommendation contained in the nine hundred-plus page Condon Study. The so-called "Condon Report" was the final report of a project which had for two years been gathering scientific data concerning UFOs under the direction of the noted physicist, Dr. Edward U. Condon.

Many people were greatly disappointed by that report, including P. J. Willcox.

After poring through the voluminous report, Willcox, an aerospace scientist who has been actively engaged in radar and optical data analyses on various projects for nearly two decades, was forced to disagree with Dr. Condon's primary conclusion and its attendant recommendations, one of the major reasons being that the majority of the scientists who supported the Condon project, and who themselves wrote major sections of the final report, recommended more investigation into the UFO phenomenon, not less. And yet, Dr. Condon (who wrote the Summary and Conclusion sections) recommended that all investigations be stopped.

Thus Willcox argues that Dr. Condon's conclusion is not supported by even the project he himself directed. This position is documented in detail in Willcox's book The UFO Question (Not Yet Answered), *published by Libra publishers.*

PQ: Sir, am I to understand that with all the interest in UFOs now, the United States Government is still not doing any investigation of this phenomenon?

PJW: That is correct, at least insofar as we know. Since 1969 there has been no identified public funding to any agency or organization to investigate UFO reports. All investigations in the last nine years have been done by small privately funded groups. Some people contend that the CIA, or perhaps some other clandestine branch of the government, is carrying on secret operations and investigations. I cannot state that there are *no* such secret activities. It is *possible* that such investigations are going on and that there is a conspiracy to keep those activities secret. However, I do not myself accept the conspiracy theory, primarily because I don't think the government or any agency thereof can keep a secret of that kind for that many years. Perhaps the explanation is as simple as that the government just doesn't know what to do with or about UFOs.

PQ: Do *you* believe that there are alien spacecraft visiting Earth?

PJW: I don't know! Out of the tens of thousands of reports, the vast majority simply do not contain enough solid information to permit a scientist to draw any sort of conclusion. One simply must discount these (except for perhaps inclusion in statistical studies that may point out trends or tendencies). There are, however, at least several dozen reports that are well documented—many of them reported by astronomers and other scientists—and many which also include radar data and/or actual optical photographs. In many of these cases there is clearly enough evidence to say that the reported UFO was not a star or planet, not a balloon or airplane, not a meteor, and not simply an optical illusion; in summary it was definitely *not* any of those things that we can readily identify as something we understand. If it was definitely not something that we do understand then the question, of course, is, what was it? In several of the cases that I've studied fairly carefully myself, they appear to have the following common characteristics: they appear to be real solid objects, they appear to be under intelligent control, and they appear to have aerodynamic capabilities beyond anything we know. In these cases the so-called extraterrestrial hypothesis appears to me to be the easiest to accept. This is simply because any other possible explanation sounds even more incredible than the extraterrestrial one.

PQ: Can you cite one of these cases?

PJW: There are many in the literature. One that has always seemed particularly significant to me is the one that has been studied in great detail by the late Dr. James McDonald, an astrophysicist from the University of Arizona. Certain aspects of this case are somewhat similar to the air control tower incident depicted in *Close Encounters of the Third Kind*.

(After reviewing his source material Mr. Willcox gave the following description based upon Dr. McDonald's account.)

The events took place over east-central England over a three hour period on the night of 13/14 August 1956. The initial report concerned a radar target which appeared on the GCA

(Ground Control Approach) radar at Bentwater. The estimated speed of the target was four thousand miles per hour, however, other relevant information yields speeds even higher (up to nine thousand mph). Several minutes later the same radar observed a group (over a dozen) of targets. They were under continuous observation for over twenty-five minutes during which time they moved relatively slowly and after which they all appeared to merge into a single, very strong, target which then remained stationary for some ten to fifteen minutes. After several more short movements with short stationary periods in between the target moved out of radar range. The third sighting came only minutes later and this time the target was a single object and moved exteremly fast; the data indicates a speed of approximately twelve thousand miles per hour. A fourth sighting by the Bentwater GCA of a two thousand to four thousand mph target traveling west resulted in their alerting the Lakenheath GCA radar sight. This target was observed by both radars as well as visually by observers on the ground. It appeared to the ground observers as a small light somewhat blurred by its motion. It was also observed visually by airborne observers in a C-47 aircraft that was flying over the area at an altitude of approximately four thousand feet. The UFO was reportedly beneath the aircraft. The same object was also observed by the RATCC (Radar Air Traffic Control Center) radar located at Lakenheath. USAF ground observers and the radar observations indicated that the object moved with extreme speed and near instantaneous changes of direction; it was also observed to remain stationary for several minutes at a time. An RAF jet interceptor scrambled to investigate also observed the target both visually and with the radar on the interceptor.

The really important thing about this case is that multiple witnesses, including four different radar systems, were involved. The characteristics of the radars are very different, which effectively rules out anomalous propagation (false targets). Likewise the credibility of the witnesses taken collectively as a group cannot be seriously questioned. The conditions of extreme speeds, unexplained maneuvers, and the fact that one UFO was simultaneously observed by two ground based radars, ground visual witnesses, one airborne radar and the one airborne witness (visually) makes this an extremely interesting and perhaps even compelling case.

PQ: What is the scientific community's attitude toward UFOs?

PJW: Although it is probably not common knowledge, there are many scientists who are doing private research or at least keeping up with the subject through reading. It is no secret, it's simply because they generally don't write popular books or for that matter publish anything at all on the subject. Actually, I would say that a large number (perhaps even a majority) of my colleagues regard UFOs as an extremely interesting subject and certainly worthy of serious investigation. Today there are more and more scientists who are publicly talking about UFOs and at the same time there appear to be fewer who criticize such interest.

PQ: Is there any kind of movement within the scientific community to obtain funding for UFO research?

PJW: Not specifically that I know of. I'm sure people have written proposals for UFO research to organizations such as the National Academy of Sciences, but none of them have been funded, at least insofar as I know. I think what is going to have to happen is that people who are known in this field, like Hynek and the Lorenzens, are going to have to get together and come up with a unified proposal stating what should be done in the next few years. So far nothing that I'm aware of has been done in that direction. Even President Carter (who himself reported a UFO sighting several years ago) asked NASA to look into the UFO question, but NASA effectively turned him down!

PQ: If people think they've actually seen a UFO, whom should they report to?

PJW: There are several major international UFO research groups headquartered in the United States. Four of the best-known are: the Center for UFO Studies (CUFOS), headed by Dr. J. Allen Hynek, a well-known astronomer (924 Chicago Ave., Evanston, Illinois 60202); The Aerial Phenomena Research Organization (APRO), headed by Jim Lorenzen (3910 E. Kleindale Rd., Tucson, Arizona 85712); the National Investigative Committee on Aerial Phenomena (NICAP), which notwithstanding its name is nonetheless a completely private group (3535 University Boulevard, West, Kensington, Maryland 20795); and the Mutual UFO Network (MUFON) (103 Oldtowne Rd., Sequin, Texas 78155).

CAST LIST

ROY NEARY
RICHARD DREYFUSS
A power repairman whose sighting of a UFO sets up a shattering chain of events that affects his family, his job and his very existence.

RONNIE NEARY
TERI GARR
Roy's wife; unable to comprehend what is happening to him, she is forced into a traumatic decision that will affect both of their lives.

JILLIAN GUILER
MELINDA DILLON
The young widow whose life and emotions are turned inside out by the unexplainable happenings in the sky.

BARRY GUILER
CARY GUFFEY
The four-year-old who holds in his mind the answers all others search for.

CLAUDE LACOMBE
FRANCOIS TRUFFAUT
The dedicated French expert of extraterrestrial life who spearheads the international "silence group."

David Laughlin
BOB BALABAN
Lacombe's
interpreter

Farmer
ROBERTS
BLOSSOM

Team Leader
MERRILL
CONNALLY

Major Benchley
GEORGE
DiCENZO

Robert
LANCE
HENRIKSEN
Lacombe's
aide

Major Walsh
WARREN
KEMMERLING
Army Security Chief

Project
Leader
J. PATRICK
McNAMARA

Brad Neary . . . . SHAWN BISHOP
Silvia Neary . . . . ADRIENNE CAMPBELL
Toby . . . . JUSTIN DREYFUSS
Ike . . . . GENE DYNARSKI
Highway Patrolman . . . . ROGER ERNEST
ARP Project Member . . . . F.J. O'NEIL
ARP Musician . . . . PHIL DODDS
Returnee #1 Flt. 19 . . . . RANDY HERMANN
Returnee #2 Flt. 19 . . . . HAL BARWOOD
Air Traffic Controller . . . . DAVID ANDERSON
Air Traffic . . . . CRAIG SHREEVE
Federalee . . . . EUMENIO BLANCO

◆

CLOSE ENCOUNTERS OF THE THIRD KIND

Sonora Desert, Mexico

Intent upon their purpose, a group of dedicated men push south through the Sierra Madre. The importance of the mission precludes any thought of rest as they arrive at their destination, a remote sand-swept village in northern Mexico. The howling sandstorm makes it difficult for them to see the waiting Mexican Federal Police.

Are we the first to arrive?

¿Qué dice?

The team leader's words are swallowed by the wind. He repeats his question.

I said,
Are we
the first
to arrive?

Sí, sí,
the first.

Shouting to be
heard over
the storm,
another of the
Federales joins
the group.

*Era algo en el
cielo, una luz muy
hermosa pero
daba mucho
miedo. La gente
estaba muy
asustada.*

What the hell is he saying? I don't understand one word. Where's that interpreter, damn it. I need him *now.*

There's another car coming. Maybe he's in it.

From the newly arrived car, several men hurry toward them, leaning into the wind.

Laughlin is moved by a curious sense of destiny as another man steps toward them through the storm.

Bonjour, *monsieur*, my name is Lacombe, and I am...

Yes sir, I know. I saw you at the conference in Montsoreau. I'm here to translate for you.

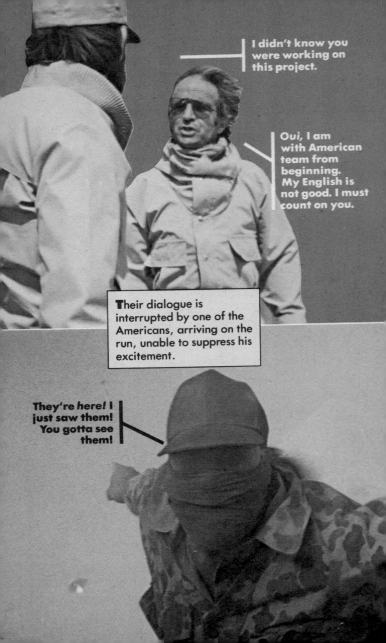

The sandstorm subsides somewhat, revealing the object of their quest, a group of vintage aircraft, circa World War II.

What the hell is happening here? Who flies crates like these anymore?

No one. These planes were reported missing in 1945. No one's seen or heard from them since then.

At Lacombe's urging, serial numbers are recorded for future verification.

M-one-four-seven-one-four-eight.

The presence of these vintage torpedo bombers in the Mexican desert poses fantastic questions. The team moves quickly through the planes—probing, checking, finding personal effects now thirty years old.

Without exception, the aircraft have charged batteries and fuel levels corresponding with mission status at the time of their disappearance.

Where are the pilots? How the hell did these planes get here? And why in the world do they look *brand new*?

Laughlin's questions remain, for the moment, unanswered, as one after another the engines of the Grumman TBM Avengers cough, catch and roar into life, mocking the howling of the storm.

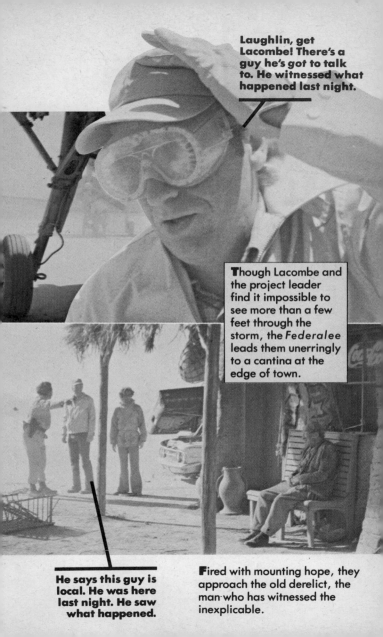

Laughlin, get Lacombe! There's a guy he's got to talk to. He witnessed what happened last night.

Though Lacombe and the project leader find it impossible to see more than a few feet through the storm, the *Federalee* leads them unerringly to a cantina at the edge of town.

He says this guy is local. He was here last night. He saw what happened.

Fired with mounting hope, they approach the old derelict, the man who has witnessed the inexplicable.

Speak to me, old man. What happened here? ¿Qué pasa?

Responding to Lacombe's gentle touch, the old man speaks softly through tears of joy.

El sol salió anoche y me cantó!

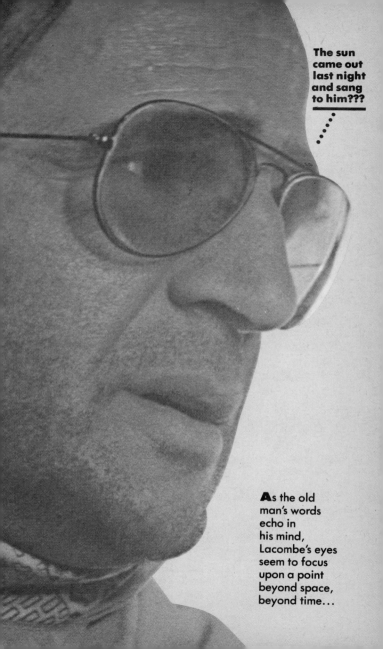

The sun came out last night and sang to him???

As the old man's words echo in his mind, Lacombe's eyes seem to focus upon a point beyond space, beyond time...

Air Traffic Control, Indianapolis Center

Three thousand miles away, in a strikingly different setting, the air traffic controllers monitor the skies above Indiana, dealing daily with hundreds of routine pilot-to-control communications. And some not so routine...

Indianapolis Center, you have any traffic for Aireast 31?

Aireast 31, negative. The only traffic I have is a TWA L-1011 in your six o'clock position. Range, fifteen miles. Also an Allegheny DC-9 in your twelve o'clock position, fifty miles. Stand by. I'll take a look at Broad Band.

Aireast 31 has traffic two o'clock, slightly above and descending.

Aireast 31, roger. I have a primary target about that position now.

The traffic's one o'clock now, still above me and descending.

Can you say aircraft type?

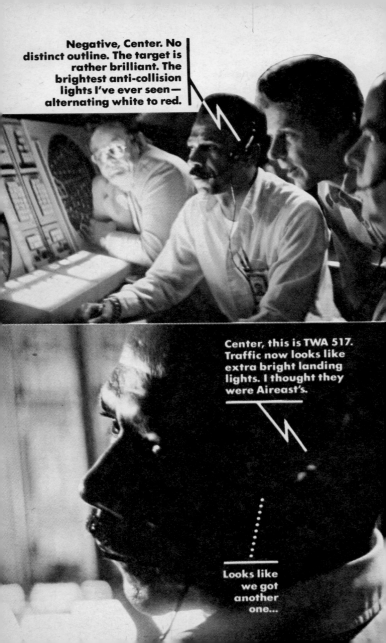

Keenly interested, the Traffic Control team crowds in close, fascinated, as the air position display moves across the screen in computer-fed increments.

Center, Aireast 31 here. The traffic has turned! He's heading right for my windshield!

Aireast 31, descend and maintain flight level three-one-zero.

Break, Allegheny triple four. Turn right thirty degrees immediately.

It's headed right by us. Right now! *Damn!* That was really close!

Ask them if they want to report it officially.

Muncie, Indiana

Not far away, the night is balmy. A soft breeze caresses the trees and rustles the curtains at the windows of a rural frame house.

Inside, a sleeper wakes from a strange dream, still remembered as consciousness creeps in.

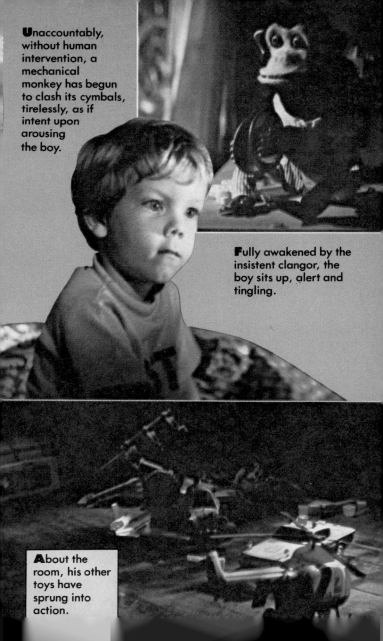

Unaccountably, without human intervention, a mechanical monkey has begun to clash its cymbals, tirelessly, as if intent upon arousing the boy.

Fully awakened by the insistent clangor, the boy sits up, alert and tingling.

About the room, his other toys have sprung into action.

A beam of light dances on the wall of the hallway, and with an irresistible sense of wonder, he follows.

Downstairs, the child walks awestruck through the house, enchanted, as the darkness outside rapidly yields to a brilliant, moving luminosity.

Drawn to the kitchen by a curious sound...

...he is confronted by an astonishing disarray.

As if called by a silent voice, the boy turns to look outside...and is suffused with an inner radiance.

And upstairs, his mother, Jillian, roused from a restless sleep by the clatter of toy cars invading her room, is puzzled to discover her light and television have been turned on.

W-what on Earth...?

Still grasping a toy car which unaccountably refuses to stop running, she enters her son's room, concerned.

Honey, where are you?

In a suburb of Muncie, power company technician Roy Neary receives an emergency call from his foreman.

Neary, get over to the Gilmore sub-station. We have lost the power up and down the line. There's some kind of drain on the primary voltage.

Sudden darkness falls as progressive power failure shuts off the lights throughout the city.

Neary enters the sub-station at a brisk walk, puzzled by the power drain, yet looking forward to the prospect of a challenging break from his routine work.

Got a fresh impedance coming up. It's not an overload; it's a drain. Lines M-Mary ten through M-Mary fifteen. And Municipal Lighting is asking to be cut free.

OK, Neary, you heard that. Grab what you need and get going. And remember, I'm depending on you.

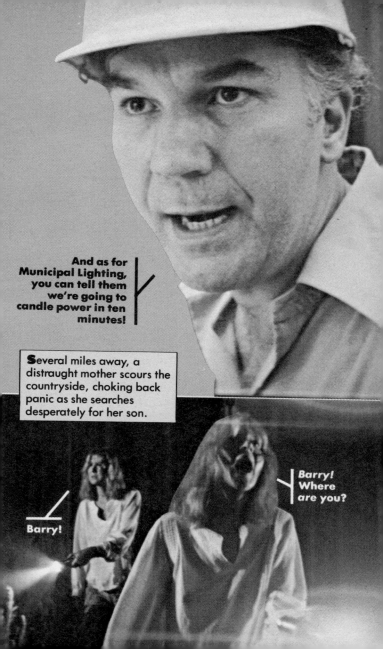

And as for Municipal Lighting, you can tell them we're going to candle power in ten minutes!

Several miles away, a distraught mother scours the countryside, choking back panic as she searches desperately for her son.

Barry!

Barry! Where are you?

Later, somewhere en route to Crystal Lake...
Where the hell am I? I must have taken a wrong turn.

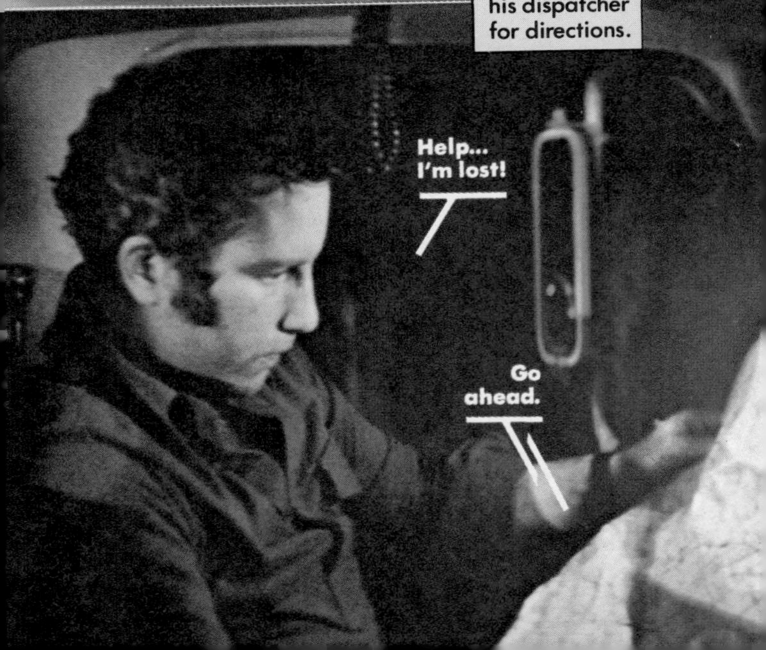
Neary radios his dispatcher for directions.
Help... I'm lost!
Go ahead.

Neary fails to notice the vehicle that has pulled up behind him until its lights illuminate the interior of his cab. Concentrating on his radio, he waves it past.

Could you cough up Tolono on Interstate 90? Maybe a familiar landmark?

Try Cornbread Road south of 20.

Cornbread, you say? Let me see if I can find that.

Studying his map, Neary is unaware that the vehicle has not gone around him, but rises instead *straight up*, displaying an array of lights unlike those of any earthly eighteen-wheeler.

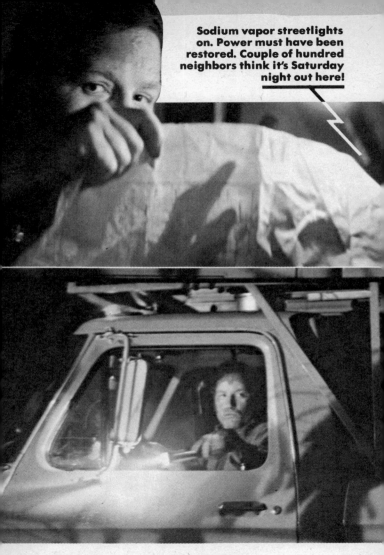

Sodium vapor streetlights on. Power must have been restored. Couple of hundred neighbors think it's Saturday night out here!

The dispatcher's message is lost as Neary's attention is caught by a rattling, chattering sound outside. He is frightfully aware of the beating of his heart as he turns his flashlight toward the source of the sound.

Despite the warmth of the night, Neary feels a chill as his light falls upon a row of rural mailboxes shuddering violently to and fro.

Suddenly, inexplicably, Neary is plunged into darkness as the flashlight, radio and all truck electricals shut down, as if a remote switch had been thrown. The mailboxes quake; a crossing signal clangs madly. Neary's mouth goes dry as he senses an overwhelming presence.

An instant later, the truck is hit with a blinding luminescence of almost palpable intensity.

Neary has difficulty breathing as the brilliance is joined by a deep, roaring vibration, suggestive of immense power.

Oh, my God!

Then, just as suddenly as it had started, it stops. The mailboxes and crossing signal cease their wild palpitations. The beam of light remains a moment before it, too, winks out, leaving a stillness accentuated by the barking of a distant dog.

Trembling, Neary peers upward, searching the night sky.

My God, look at the size of that thing!

Seconds later, a stop sign up the road is illuminated from above by a narrow beam of solar intensity. But only for a moment. Then darkness.

At the edge of panic, Neary finds himself unable to move, as the interior of the cab becomes a raging maelstrom of flying debris.

Jesus, what the *hell* is going on???

But he stiffens with interest as a flood of calls spills out of the radio.

I don't believe this! It's big as a house.

It's crazy! Shaped like a barn.

It's just off the Tolono Expressway ...east toward Harper Valley.

Driven by a compulsion he does not yet understand, Neary takes off in pursuit.

Responding to something deeper than thought, he pushes the truck to its limit.

Hurtling through the night, he begins to know the meaning of obsession, as the thing he has seen obliterates all other thoughts in his mind.

Going flat out now, Neary feels an excitement unique in his experience as he speeds closer to the possibility of another encounter.

Meanwhile, Barry's late night trek has brought him to a remote country road. Unafraid, he smiles and waves at a group of people gathered there.

There is an air about them, something peaceful and friendly, as they welcome the approach of the little stranger.

Frantic, Jill scrambles onto the road a moment later, just a split second before...

...Neary's truck, driven with reckless disregard, careens around the bend.

Barry!!!

Fighting for control, Neary stands on the brakes as he sees the woman flash in front of him in a headlong tackle, sweeping the child from his path.

Wrenching the wheel hard over, Neary brings the truck to a standstill against a fence and stumbles, shaking, across the road.
Oh my God, are you OK? I'm sorry. I didn't even see him until you ran out.

Breaking free from his mother's grasp, the boy dashes into the road, calling out to the sky.
Hello. Come here. Play with me.
My God, what's the matter with him?

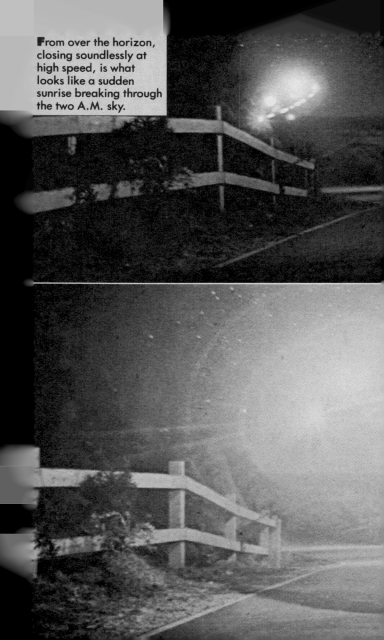

From over the horizon, closing soundlessly at high speed, is what looks like a sudden sunrise breaking through the two A.M. sky.

Frozen with awe, the group stands open-mouthed as a fabulous light show sweeps past them, flying low over the road...

...followed by another of utterly different configuration, its brilliantly coruscating lights putting to shame any Christmas ornament devised by man.

Neary feels a prickling on his face and the stirring of a nascent joy deep within him.

There is something akin to gaiety in the graceful way the objects skim overhead.

And, as the flashing, twinkling display recedes, the spectators remember to breathe again.

A moment later, like a will-o'-the-wisp, a glowing red orb dances above the road, following an erratic path after the other flying objects, reminding Neary for an instant of Tinker Bell.

Ice cream!

The shining objects vanish around the bend. The watchers are unaware that the crickets have resumed their song, only to stop again as an undulating wailing approaches from the east.

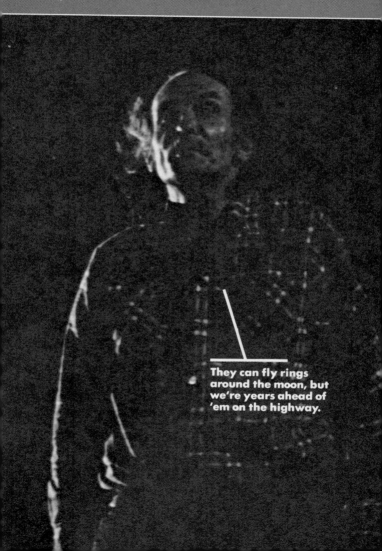

There is an odd mixture of reverence and familiarity in the old man's voice as he speaks.

They can fly rings around the moon, but we're years ahead of 'em on the highway.

Just in time, Neary shoves Jill and Barry off the road as three police cars scream around the curve at well over one hundred miles per hour.

Without conscious decision, Neary runs to his truck, slams into gear and follows, adding two more strips of rubber to those already on the road.

I've got to know what they are!

At the rear of the high-speed caravan, Neary closes the gap with the police. And in the first patrol car the driver keeps his eyes locked on the flying lights and his foot jammed on the accelerator.

Jesus, look at that! Look at those suckers. They're glued to the road!

The scintillating objects that had hugged the curve of the road so closely since the chase began suddenly decide to leave it at a hairpin curve. With a fantastic increase in speed they shoot up over the guardrail and into the heavens.

An instant later, the pursuit car, with the driver mesmerized by the radiant ensemble ahead, follows them through the guardrail and becomes airborne for one long moment before bouncing off the embankment and landing in the ravine below.

With their brakes nearly on fire, Neary and the police skid to a stop at the cliffside, unable to take their eyes from the spectacular lights in the sky, now fused into a single glowing orb receding rapidly.

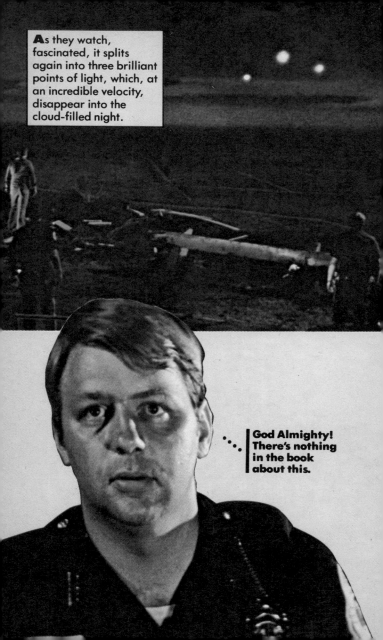

As they watch, fascinated, it splits again into three brilliant points of light, which, at an incredible velocity, disappear into the cloud-filled night.

God Almighty! There's nothing in the book about this.

For a timeless moment, the clouds into which the objects have climbed are illuminated from within. And, as the swirling night fire fades from the sky, Roy Neary can see lights coming on across the horizon. Tolono...Crystal Lake... Harper Valley...Muncie. The blackout is over.

Jesus Christ! That's the most incredible thing I ever saw!

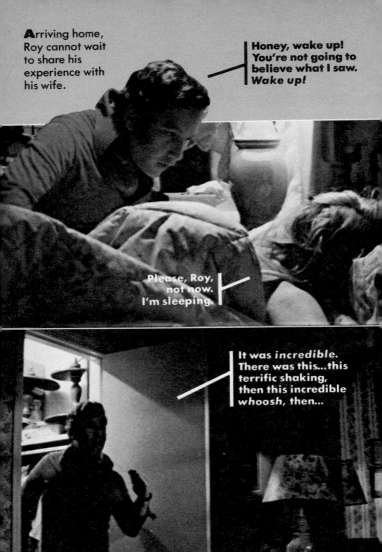

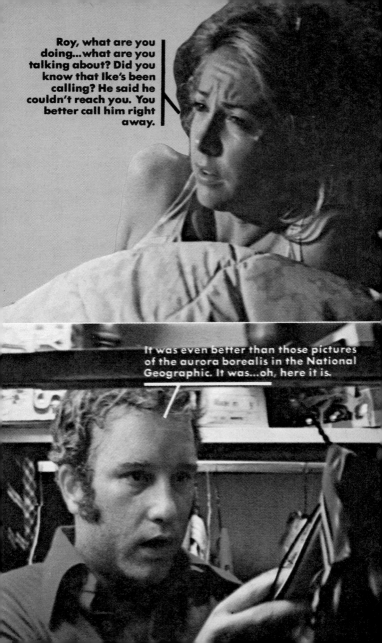

Come on, Ronnie, get up.
Are you nuts? It's four o'clock in the morning.
Well, you're always saying you want to get out of the house.
Ronnie, I need you to see something with me. Please. It's really important.

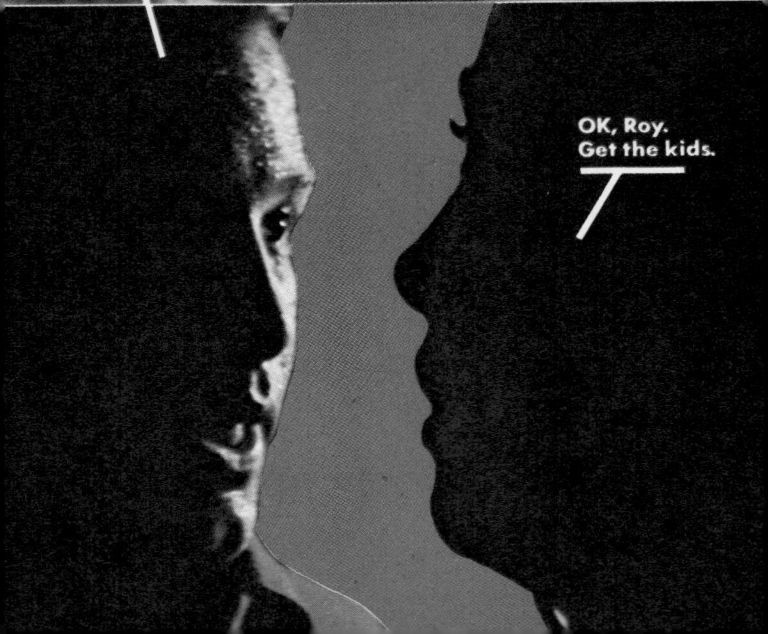
OK, Roy. Get the kids.

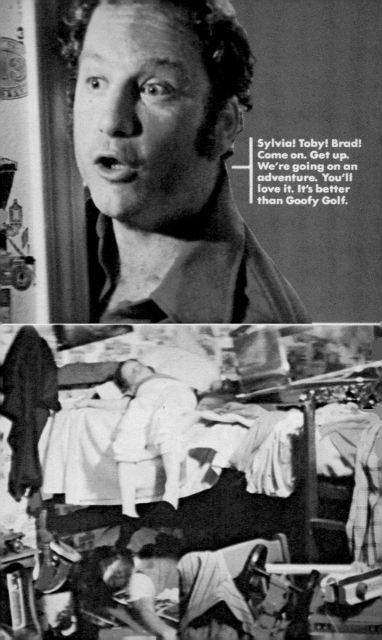

Sylvia! Toby! Brad! Come on. Get up. We're going on an adventure. You'll love it. It's better than Goofy Golf.

Bundling his family into the truck…

Roy, your face! It's…it's sunburned. What happened to you?

Wow! That's amazing. Don't worry about it. I'll explain everything.

Returning to the spot where he had seen the indescribable coruscating objects, Roy and Ronnie step onto the road, leaving their children fast asleep inside the truck.

It was like an ice cream cone...and it wasn't. It was like, ah, like...

Don't you think I'm taking this really well?

I remember when we used to come to places like this just to look at each other...

...and snuggle.

But Roy's mind is in the skies, with a growing awareness that his life has been somehow transformed by what he has witnessed that night. For him, nothing will ever be the same again.

The following morning Ronnie discovers a most intriguing article in the local paper.

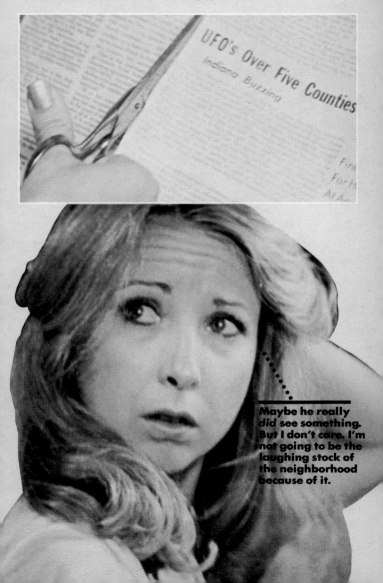

UFO's Over Five Counties

Indiana Buzzing

Maybe he really did see something. But I don't care. I'm not going to be the laughing stock of the neighborhood because of it.

In the bathroom,
preparing to shave, Roy
gets his first clear look
at his half-burned face.

Jesus, I
look like a
50-50 Bar!

Something about the
mound of shaving
cream captures and
holds his attention.

This shape...
like something
I know...
but what?

Ronnie's initial lack of enthusiasm gives way to open hostility as the day wears on.

Dad, tell me again what they were like.

Now, stop that, both of you! I've *had it* with this whole stupid story!

But Dad said—

I don't care what he said! I don't want to hear about this anymore. Now go outside and play.

Ronnie, no matter what you think...what you say...I can't just pretend it didn't happen.

Later that day, an unexpected phone call drives still another wedge between them.

That was your boss. He didn't even want to talk to you. He just said you were fired. Didn't I tell you to call in?

I want you to know I'm not going to get a job. I'm not going to go to work, so don't even ask.

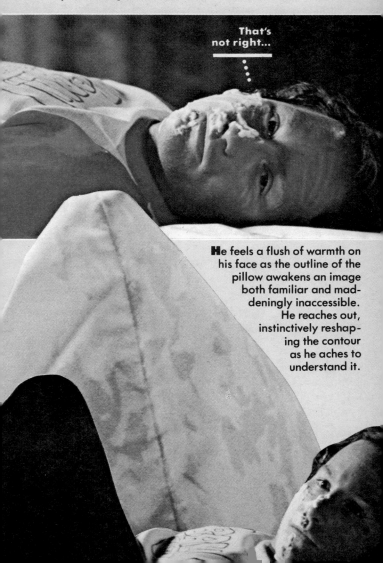

Roy lies, withdrawn, and Ronnie's voice seems muted by distance, as the elusive significance of the shaving cream is echoed by something else on the bed.

That's not right...

He feels a flush of warmth on his face as the outline of the pillow awakens an image both familiar and maddeningly inaccessible. He reaches out, instinctively reshaping the contour as he aches to understand it.

Focusing on the shape the boy is molding, Roy is jolted by a flash of recognition.

He feels it too. It's the same shape... *almost.*

Absorbed, Barry pats mud into place purposefully—forming, shaping, intent upon his task.

Neary kneels beside the boy. There is an air of tacit understanding as he too starts to work on the mound, correcting... helping.

Roy's reverie is interrupted by shouts springing from the crowd, as powerful lights are spotted through the hazy sky.

Here they come again!

I see them! They're coming from the northwest.

It's like Halloween for grownups.

Trick or treat!

Blinded by the brightness of the lights, they can hear a chattering, vibrating roar as they await the approach of the thing in the sky.

The staccato roar is deafening now as it skims the treetops. A surge of adrenaline runs through the crowd.

STOP AND BE FRIENDLY

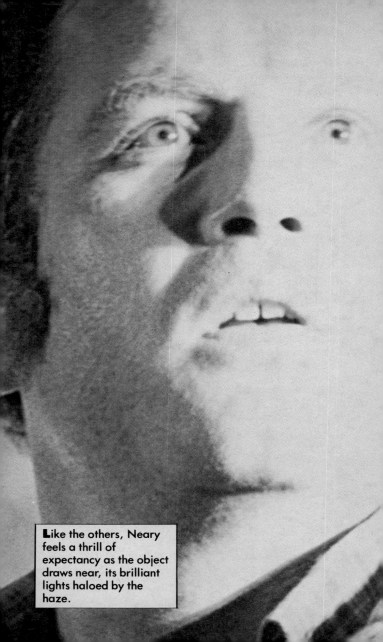

Like the others, Neary feels a thrill of expectancy as the object draws near, its brilliant lights haloed by the haze.

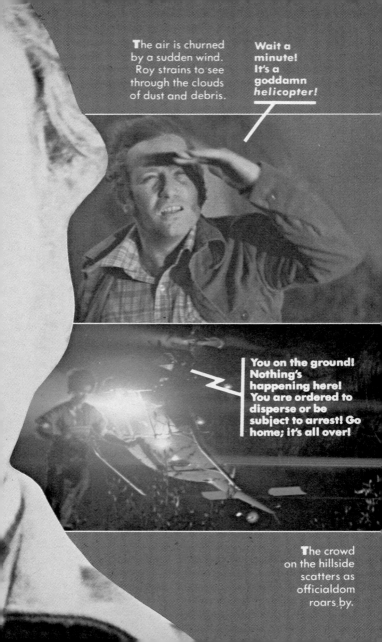

Dharmsala, Northern India

Shimmering in the heat, saffron, white and ecru robes dot a hillside in remote northern India, as a multitude of devout Hindus gather to await the arrival of foreign visitors on a special quest. A rhythmic chanting wells up from the throng: five notes, over and over, echoing across the plain.

Mais, c'est la guerre pentatonique...cinq notes au lieu de sept.

He says it's the pentatonic war. That old musical controversy between the five and seven note scales.

The Brahman leader welcomes Lacombe openly, sensing more than he has been told of the reasons that have brought the Frenchman halfway around the world.

Demandez-lui d'ou viennent ces sons.

He would like to know, From what direction did your people hear these sounds?

The Brahman leader translates Lacombe's question for the old Hindu now joining them.

Kis taraf se tumerey logo ko yai awaz aay?

Turning with what might be a smile, the old man calls out to the crowd below, repeating the question.

A crash of sound resounds through the hills as thousands answer as one, with one gesture, one voice.

ISSEY UPPAR!!

One week later, Lacombe excitedly addresses a much smaller group in the United States.

Good evening, ladies and gentlemen. *Parlez-vous Français?*

Well, my English is not good too. But I want to share with you now the breakthrough that happened in India.

We think
it means
something...
something
important.

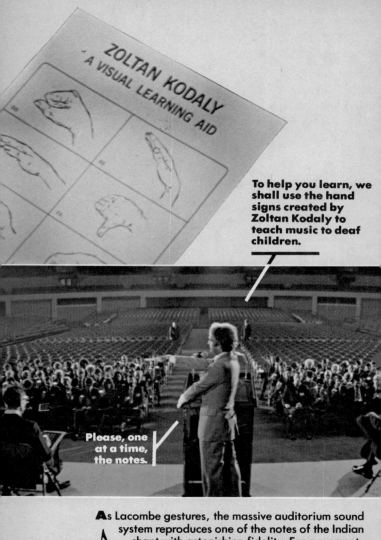

ZOLTAN KODALY
A VISUAL LEARNING AID

To help you learn, we shall use the hand signs created by Zoltan Kodaly to teach music to deaf children.

Please, one at a time, the notes.

As Lacombe gestures, the massive auditorium sound system reproduces one of the notes of the Indian chant with astonishing fidelity. For a moment, Lacombe is transported in thought to Dharmsala, and thousands of Hindu voices fill the hall.

One by one, at Lacombe's signal each of the five notes of the chant are played for the audience.

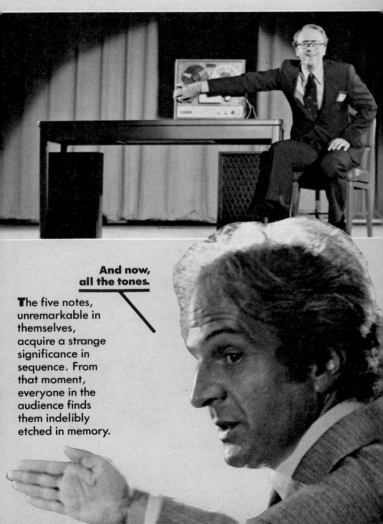

And now, all the tones.

The five notes, unremarkable in themselves, acquire a strange significance in sequence. From that moment, everyone in the audience finds them indelibly etched in memory.

Goldstone Radio Telescope
Station 14

Lacombe's schedule is tight. And in Barstow, California, his arrival is eagerly awaited by a group of specialists within a top-security missile tracking complex.

Where's Lacombe?
I don't know
what to make
of those readouts.

He'll be here.
He's never late

Arriving a moment later, the Frenchman is bustled into the mobile glass cubicle crammed with telemetry tracking hardware, command consoles...and an ARP synthesizer.

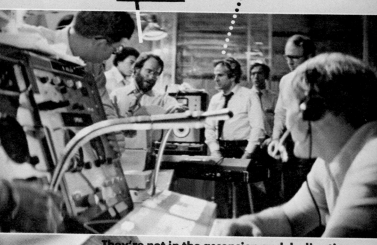

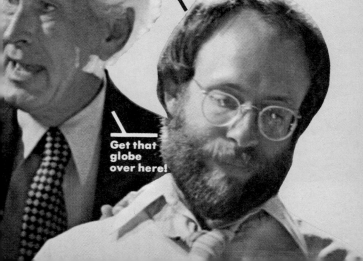

Finding the line of latitude, one of the men traces his finger along it from west to east. Another man locates the longitude at the pole and follows it until their fingers meet.

I want a Geodetic Survey map of Wyoming. I want this down to the square mile.

Lacombe's voice is charged with optimism as he calls out from the receiving console.

Ecoutez!
Listen!
I'm getting some infor-mation now.

Someone clears his throat, underlining the silence in the cubicle as Lacombe sits at the synthesizer. The Frenchman's hand is rock steady as he fingers the five-note sequence.

As dusk blankets Indiana, the same five notes are heard in the Guiler household as Barry taps them out on his toy xylophone.

Wrapped in concentration, a distant look comes into his eyes as he repeats the sequence over and over.

Jillian has been sketching again, as she had when Barry's father was alive. She can't say why, but these sketches are all of mountains, from her imagination...or from a dimly remembered dream. On an impulse she decides to throw them out. All but one.

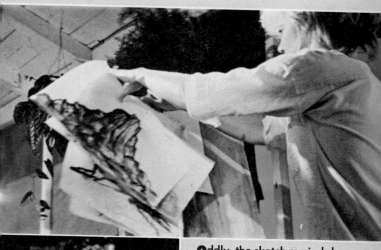

Oddly, the sketch reminds her of the notes Barry is playing on his little xylophone. He stops playing. And turning, she sees him staring through the screen.

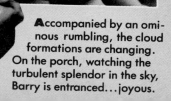

Accompanied by an ominous rumbling, the cloud formations are changing. On the porch, watching the turbulent splendor in the sky, Barry is entranced...joyous.

In the east, the clouds become turgid with a roiling magnificence both beautiful and disturbing. Jill's breath is sucked from her lungs as a deep roaring fills the night. Frightened, she hurries inside.

Stalked by panic and feeling besieged, Jill wedges a chair against the kitchen door and rushes through the house, locking windows, pulling down shades.

While Barry is drawn, irresistibly, to the front door.

Knifing through the keyhole, a beam of radiant energy seems to beckon him.

Jill dashes toward her son, bowing her head against the glare, fantastically brilliant now as if a sun has chosen to become a nova on their porch.

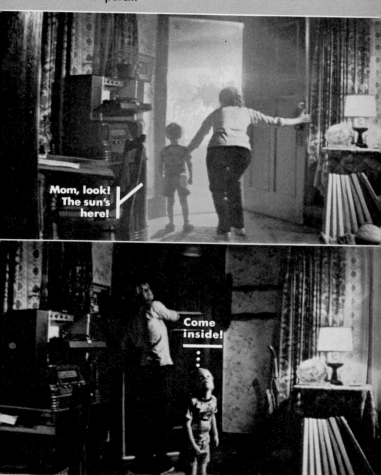

Snatching him inside, she shuts the door against an almost fluid resistance.

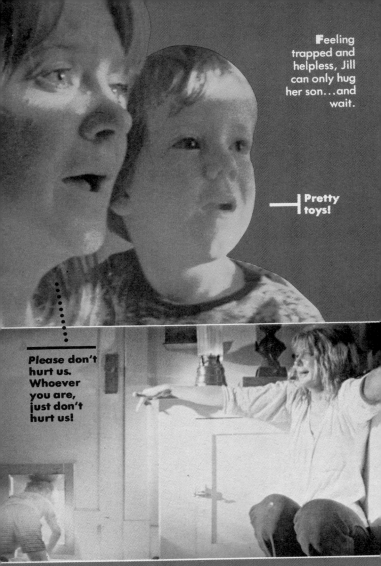

Feeling trapped and helpless, Jill can only hug her son...and wait.

Pretty toys!

Please don't hurt us. Whoever you are, just don't hurt us!

The roaring is deafening now. And Jill yields to panic as the floor seems to sway beneath her feet. Motivated beyond his understanding, Barry heads for the outside.

Horrified, Jill lunges for his legs, exerting all her strength and more in an effort to pull him back inside — without avail as, inexorably, he is ripped from her grasp by an overwhelming force.

Manic, sobbing, she flings open the door, to find him gone. And the luminous clouds fold in upon themselves and recede into the night.

In response to a landslide of sightings and mounting public pressure, the Air Force has arranged a press conference to allay suspicion of official complicity and secrecy.

You may all go in now. Room 3655. Major Benchley will speak to you.

UNITED STATES AIR FORCE

MRS. DORGAN

Now, *maybe*, we'll get some answers.

Ladies and gentlemen, I call your attention to this photograph of a flying saucer taken by me earlier today.

The reason I am so positive that it is indeed a flying saucer is because the photograph was taken of this pewter saucer tossed up in the air by one of my children.

I put this little
demonstration together t[o]
point out that our eyes ca[n]
deceive us. Last year
Americans took seven
billion photographs, yet
do not have one shot that [is]
indisputable photograph[ic]
evidence.

What a
bunch of
baloney!

Sir, it would be easy to say yes to that. But I'm not going to mislead you. This is just not the case. I don't know what you saw.

You can't fool us by agreeing with us.

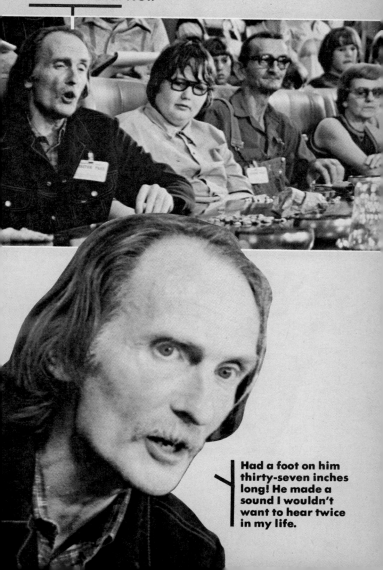

I saw Bigfoot once. Back in Sequoia National Park in 1951.

Had a foot on him thirty-seven inches long! He made a sound I wouldn't want to hear twice in my life.

They can talk
till they're blue
in the face. . . . . .
I saw them.
And Jill saw
them too.

The official
platitudes, catch
phrases and
assurances wash over
Neary unheard. His
mind is on what he
has seen and...

COSMIC KIDNAPIN

Indiana Woman Blames Disa
of Three-Year-Old Son on

...on something
else, unseen
yet familiar.

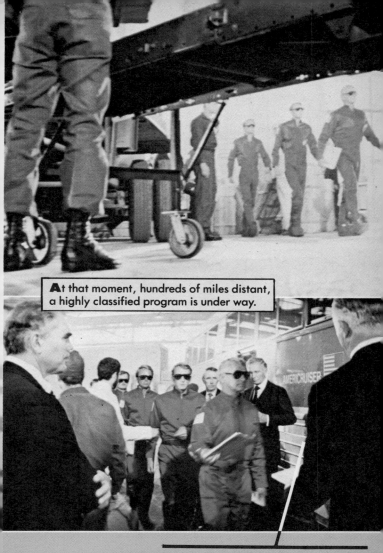

At that moment, hundreds of miles distant, a highly classified program is under way.

Let's get in touch with those Forest Service people. I don't want to end up in that wilderness with vehicular traffic. That's strictly sacred cow stuff for those people in Wyoming.

In the same facility, another group works on an essential detail of the project.

Nah, we can't use flash floods. There's a drought out there.

What about an epidemic?

You mean the plague? Who's going to believe that in this day and age?

What I need is something so scary it'll clear three hundred square miles of every living Christian soul!

The men loading the truck have all been cleared through Security to the level of Secret, yet they have no idea of the nature of the mission or why they have been ordered to camouflage the trucks as commercial vehicles.

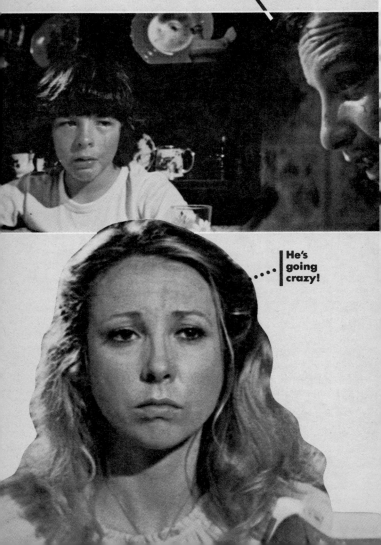

That night, working in clay rather than mashed potatoes, Roy strives to reproduce the shape with which he has become completely possessed.

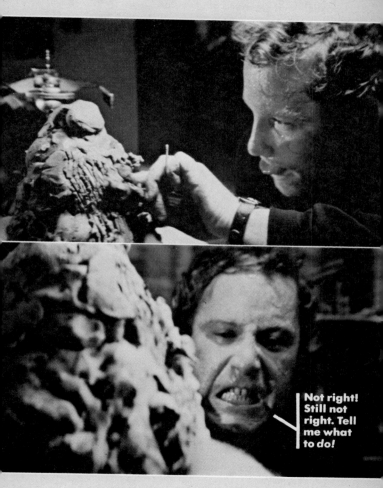

Not right! Still not right. Tell me what to do!

Frustrated beyond endurance after hours of fruitless work, Neary attacks the mound, releasing his fury upon the clay. Passive, malleable, it seems to mock him with its silence.

After a restless night spent pursuing the elusive image in his dreams, Roy wakes to daylight and the sound of television.

Anxious to be rid of the symbol of his obsession, he rips the top from the mound... and is stunned by what remains.

My God, that's it!!

Several miles away, watching the same channel, Jillian too has a sudden awakening.

Due to a strong prevailing north-south wind, the Wyoming National Guard and Army Chemical Engineers are evacuating almost two hundred square miles. Everyone is being warned to stay out of the area.

That's it! It's the same.

It's the same mountain!

It's what
I've been
seeing
all along!

And the five-note
sequence echoes
through her mind
once again.

Moorcroft, Wyoming

Having driven a rented car straight through from Muncie, Neary arrives in Wyoming.

...ten thousand others are homeless. The U.S. Army Material Command has issued these new area restrictions: All roadways north...

Why aren't there any fat lines instead of all these thin ones?

The depot is a bustle of activity with street vendors hawking their wares in the crush of thousands anxious to depart, all under the watchful eye of the United States Army.

Folks, this G-M nerve gas is odorless and colorless. These birds are guaranteed to keel over an hour before you do.

Evacuees whose last name begins with "K" through "P," as in Peter, all aboard, please.

Trying to get past the guards, Neary invents a missing sister.

Nah, I don't need any help. I'll just look around for her.

Fella, we got orders to *shoot* anybody looting around here. So, go back where you came from.

Feeling a little foolish, Roy buys a couple of gas masks and a brace of "guaranteed-to-keel-over-before-you-do" pigeons.

Seems stupid, but I might as well play it safe.

Neary searches through the thousands crowding the depot with a certainty born of intuition.

She's here... somewhere. I *know* she is.

The roads are effectively blocked, and after being turned back a few times...

The only way we're going to get back in there is to go across country.

Let's go!

Fence after fence falls to the station wagon as they sail across country, sometimes bottoming out... sometimes airborne. Roy and Jill feel exultant.

Shortly, nearing Devil's Tower, they encounter the bodies of sheep littering the meadows, triggering second thoughts.

Look, I guarantee you that this whole thing is a put-on. They can't pull the wool over our eyes with a few dead sheep!

Definitely!

With a quick exchange of glances, the masks are donned in record time.

Hey... I paid for these things...

Yeah, you might as well get your money's worth.

Rounding a curve a few minutes later, Neary brakes to a stop. The road is blocked by vehicles and an armed and anonymous group of men, apparently shocked to see them within the perimeter of quarantine.

Taken politely, but firmly, into custody, Jill and Roy are separated and removed by a van to a "decontamination center" with the look of a staging area.

Brimming with questions, Neary is taken to a small room and subjected to an intense and searching scrutiny.

Demandez-lui pourquoi il s'est éxpose aux gaz toxiques?

We have very little time, Mr. Neary. We need honest and direct answers.

Why have you purposely exposed yourself to the toxic gas?

You know as well as I do that there's nothing wrong with the air.

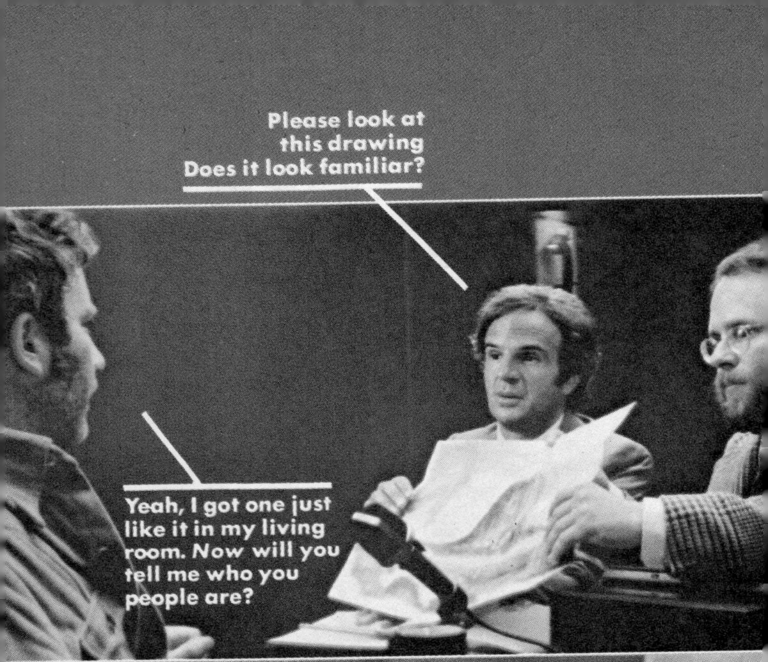
Please look at this drawing Does it look familiar?
Yeah, I got one just like it in my living room. Now will you tell me who you people are?

A-t'-il eu des rencontre plutôt inhabituelle?
One more question, please. Have you recently had a close encounter with something very unusual?

Yes, her I know.

What did you two expect to find here?

An answer. That's not crazy, is it?

They're talking French so I won't understand. Jesus, I hate that!

Lacombe explains to Laughlin that he intuitively trusts Neary and the other pilgrims caught within the perimeter, believing them to be chosen, by chance.

Abruptly, the interview is over. Helped into his gas mask and flanked by guards, Neary is walked across the compound.

Hey! I didn't come this far just to be taken on any bus ride home.

Soon he finds himself being helped into a crew transport helicopter along with the others who had penetrated this far.

Anxiously looking around, Roy finds comfort...

...in a familiar face.

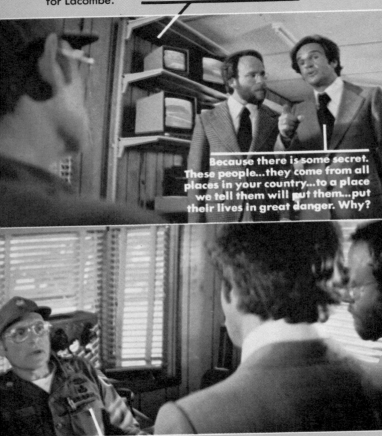

Major Walsh, in charge of the military end of the project, has sent for Lacombe.

You brought twelve people to the decontamination camp instead of the evacuation center where they belong. I'd like to know why.

Because there is some secret. These people...they come from all places in your country...to a place we tell them will put them...put their lives in great danger. Why?

I'll tell you why. Because somebody could be trying to subvert this whole operation by sending in fanatics and cultists and Christ knows what all.

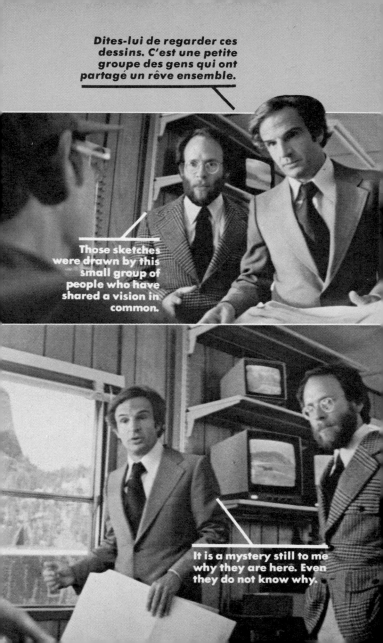

Refusing to accept the poison gas hoax, Roy pulls off his mask.

Don't! That air will kill you!

Roy takes a shallow breath... then fills his lungs.

There's *nothing* wrong with the air around here. The army's getting us out of here because they don't want any witnesses.

I also do not know what is happening, but I must discover ...find the reason.

I believe that for every person that did come here, many... hundreds who could not come also had the vision.

It's just a coincidence. It's not scientific.

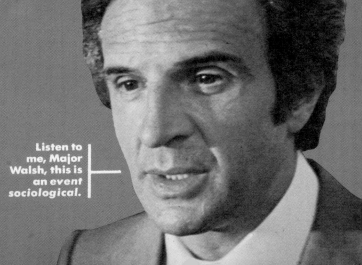

Listen to me, Major Walsh, this is an *event* sociological.

One man opts for escape with Roy and Jill. And they're off.

Go for the mountain!

Glancing outside at that instant, the Frenchman manages to remain silent, suppressing a gasp of joy, as he sees the trio headed for Devil's Tower.

Roy, Jill and Larry, their fellow escapee, rush up the slope, heedless of the hue and cry behind them.

I remember from my sketches a ravine that leads straight up. It's an easier climb.

No good. When you get to the top, it's a three hundred foot drop straight down.

At the command post, search teams are deployed in support of helicopters already in the air...and other measures are discussed.

If you can't get those folks out of the area by twenty hundred hours, start dusting with that sleep aerosol. You didn't use it all up on that livestock, did you?

No, sir. Riot control supplied us with plenty.

Ground troops join in the search, combing the mountain on foot.

Nothing to report except that there's at least a thousand places to hide. We'll need three times the men if you want this area covered in an hour.

OK, get everybody off the northern face and call the dark side of the moon and tell them we're going to dust.

On the mountain, Roy and Jill press on, unwilling to stop, as Larry, his heart beating from the climb, pauses to rest. Lacking the strength to move, he watches the approach of another helicopter.

I'll rest for just a minute.

From their hidden position above, Roy and Jill can see something different about this one. Something threatening.

Larry, don't let them see you. Get down. *Get down!*

Instinctively, they hold their breath as the helicopter, like some nightmarish sandman, makes its pass over Larry, releasing a cloud of soporific dust.

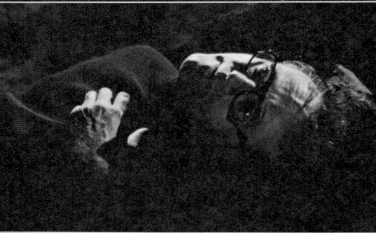

Inhaling the dust, Larry sags to the rocks, already drifting off.

Just the two of us now... so close to knowing.

As they near the top, a bright glow from the eastern slope provides a course correction. And they're running now toward the light.

Crawling, scrabbling, pulling each other along and up, Roy and Jillian make their ascent. And, rounding the pinnacle, they are rewarded with an astonishing sight.

Do you see that?

Oh, yes ...yes ...yes!

I knew it! This is important. I've got to get down there!

Trying to grasp what they see, Roy and Jill stare open-mouthed as a voice from a loudspeaker carries to them over the warm night air.

Gentlemen...ladies...Take your positions, please. This is not a drill. I repeat, this is not a drill. Can we have the lights in the arena down sixty percent, please. I don't think we could ask for a more beautiful evening, do you?

Roy has to agree. It is the most beautiful night he has known...ever.

OK, watch the sky, please. We now show uncorrelated targets approaching from the north northwest.

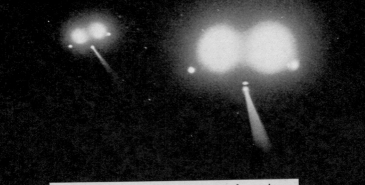

Jill moves a little closer to Roy as, from above and behind them, two refulgent objects, like flamboyant comets, split the sky and streak toward the runway below...

...followed a second later by a lamping red orb, dancing in the wake of the other two, like some cosmic firefly.

At positions circling the site, camera crews run through operability check lists. Pin-registered and rotating-prism high-speed cameras are ready.

Above the runway, drowning the floodlights with their lightsome splendor, the shining objects indulge in dazzling aerobatics. And below, the site is alive with activity.

All ground personnel, not Final-Phase approved, please evacuate the center of the program mock-up. Audio analysis personnel, behind the yellow double line.

Computer technicians lift their eyes from their control boards to the flashing, lambent flames dancing over the runway.

ITC stereo time and resistance audio ready. Tone interpolation and interlock.

Key interlock... *now!* Speed set at seven and a half. All positive functions. Standing by.

As lights fade from the western sky, the scintillating objects come closer, low over the runway made obsolete by their presence.

Sunset ...Go!

OK, start with the tone.

Up a full tone.

At the signal, a clear synthesized note soars up from the network of powerful speakers surrounding the runway.

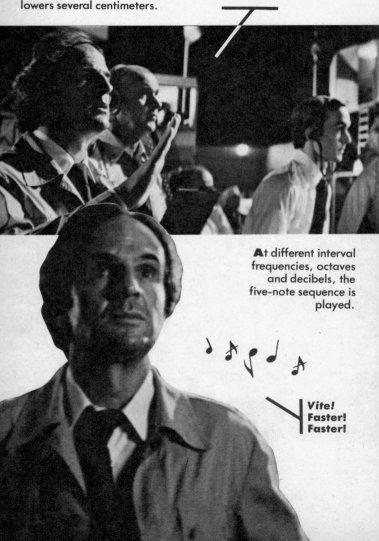

With his eyes on the three sparkling objects, the team leader can see Lacombe's hand in the periphery of his vision as it lowers several centimeters.

Now drop an octave.

At different interval frequencies, octaves and decibels, the five-note sequence is played.

Vite! Faster! Faster!

The organist
increases the
tempo, with his
eyes fixed, as if
hypnotized, on
the shining shapes...

...while his hands,
autonomous, pick out the
notes Lacombe first heard
in Dharmsala.

The night air is filled
with music as the
three ships seem to
dance above the
runway.

Then, separating, they leap heavenward and disappear into the stars.

The glittering craft leave a lustrous afterglow. Watching it, Roy feels the pounding of his pulse, tempered by a calm certainty flowing outward from his core.

Lacombe and the others at the rendezvous point feel a thrill of exuberance at this festive, firsthand evidence of response, even as a prickling of imminence brushes their senses.

Moving fast, a cloud of Olympian magnificence uncoils from behind Devil's Tower, changing shape as it advances.

And, from behind the peak, a radiant aurora halos the crest.

Closer to the site, Roy and Jill can hear a babel of voices as another of the brilliant craft begins a low pass over the runway.

C'mon, keep down!

A number of the spacecraft are visible now, buzzing the field.

Magnifique! But the aliens themselves...if only we could see them...speak with them...

Squinting against the lights and rising wind, Neary looks on with a rush of joy as a luminescent squadron comes in from the east at incredible velocity.

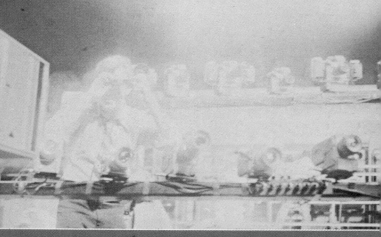

The dazzling ships close in on the base, passing low and very fast, leaving a flash of afterimages in their wake. Banks of still and motion picture cameras vibrate and shake, as once did a row of mailboxes in rural Indiana.

The project personnel hit the deck as the blazing craft buzz the field like impish heralds of yet another ship now nearing the runway.

Jeez! That was close!

The shining craft pass even closer over Roy and Jill, but their attention is divided by the ship now slowing over the site.

Look at that! Will you look at that?

Like a galactic Goodyear blimp, the ship drifts slowly overhead, a splendor of sparkling light.

A flood of light, like a candescent Niagara, bathes the field as the craft hovers low. And technicians work zealously, recording on tape and film.

Fantastic! Keep those reloads coming.

Other craft are coming in now, fantastic and
glimmering, shining their lights on the base,
bedazzling and somehow inspiring.

They kiss quickly, impulsively, and, from her position on the slope, Jill watches as Roy makes his way to the edge of the base.

This is data control to all personnel: We monitor no biological hazards. Range: Safety clear.

Lacombe is the first to feel it—a deep rumbling vibration in the lower registers, awesome and suggestive of the nearness of an incredible energy. Some instinct causes the Frenchman to look up at Devil's Tower.

A split instant later Neary feels it too. And, for a frozen moment, his pulse stops.

The rumbling is thunderous now. And, like a celestial sunrise, a glittering exaltation of light rises over Devil's Tower.

The sheer size of it is heartstopping, blotting out the stars with its immensity — the largest craft ever seen by man.

Those on the ground can only stare, agape, as the vessel descends slowly toward them, revolving about its vertical axis.

The ship of light draws near, and the effect is one of staggering beauty, destined to change forever the lives of all who witness its radiant splendor.

There are some whose lives are marked beyond comprehension. Neary's first glimpse of the ship is a shock of satori.

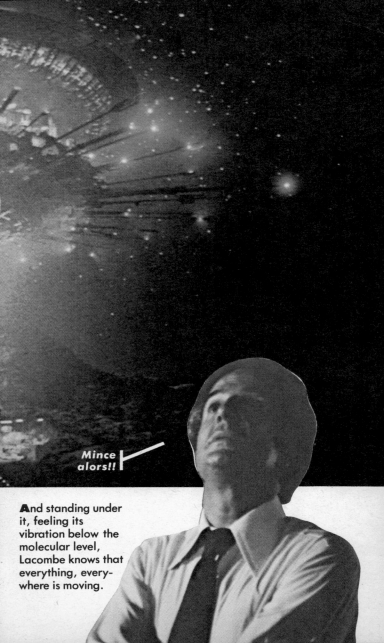

Mince alors!!

And standing under it, feeling its vibration below the molecular level, Lacombe knows that everything, everywhere is moving.

At close range, the light from the ship is dazzling, even through the dark glasses now worn by most of those present.

There is a safety hazard zone extending twenty-five meters from the ship. Special teams are exempt and should be aware of low gravity.

Despite hours of rehearsal, those on the ground find themselves surging forward as the great ship nears touchdown.

Expect some dizziness and look out for static charge.

Looking on from the slope, Jill too is drawn forward.

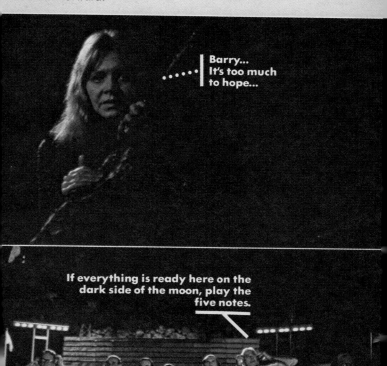

Barry...
It's too much
to hope...

If everything is ready here on the dark side of the moon, play the five notes.

All departments operational during this phase, please signify.

The familiar tonal sequence wells out again from the speakers surrounding and facing the ship. And, in response, a deep bass rumbling emanates from the huge vessel.

Vibrating around the lower rim, lights flash in concert with the deep five-note pattern coming from the ship in great booming waves of sound, dwarfing yet complementing those played upon the synthesizer.

She sent us four quavers, a group of five quavers, a group of four semi-quavers.
Give her six quavers, then pause.
What are we saying to each other?
It seems they're trying to teach us a tonal vocabulary.
It's the first day of school, fellas.

The musical conversation continues, and the air is festooned with sound.

Jill is on the runway now, hurrying toward the ship.

Even for those who have followed the quest from the start, the significance of contact is just beginning to unfold.

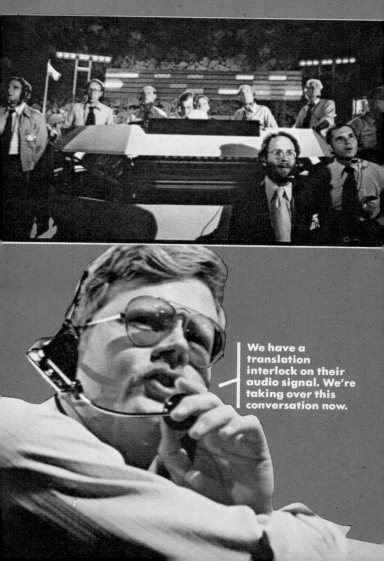

We have a translation interlock on their audio signal. We're taking over this conversation now.

With the achievement of translation interlock status, communication begins in earnest. Even those without access to the tonal interpretation readouts can read between the lines as the notes take on a quality of joy...and friendship.

My God! They're here... They're really here!

The notes subside as, gently, the mammoth ship touches Earth. And, for a moment, all is quiet.

A panel in the belly
of the ship slides
open, revealing a glare
of purest white.

The light falls upon them like
a benediction. And, as they
watch, the panel slides smoothly
down and becomes a ramp.

Something is emerging from the ship and, striving to see through the brilliance, the crowd leans forward, unable to take another step, held back by deference and awe. Only one man dares to move.

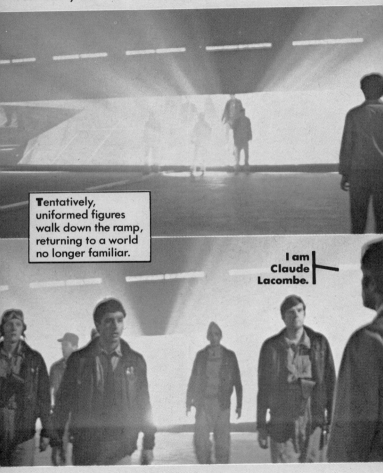

Tentatively, uniformed figures walk down the ramp, returning to a world no longer familiar.

I am Claude Lacombe.

Frank Taylor, Lieutenant J. G., United States Naval Reserve, 064199.

Jill moves past the crowd, toward the light...then breaks into a run...

...as another figure walks, smiling, down the ramp.

People continue to step off the ramp. And, as they do, their names are checked off against lists of the missing.

Lacombe, having left Neary's side, finds Laughlin.

Quickly! We must plead Neary's case. There is not much time.

Neary doesn't hear him speak as he returns
to his side. The humans have disembarked
and something else is moving down the ramp.

I envy you.

The crowd takes a step back,
even Lacombe and Neary, as a
figure comes into view.

Long and sinewy, it moves with a slow grace, regarding them.

Other humanoid figures, smaller and without the messianic dignity of the first, follow...

...to stand on the Earth itself, facing the humans...

...with searching interest, across a space of a few meters.

Deeply moved and touched with a curious ecstasy, the Earth people stand staring at the aliens. Their thoughts are filled with wonder...and questions...

...questions which, for some, never needed asking.

There is movement behind the humans facing the ramp. Fulfilling their wildest hopes, the primary objective of the rendezvous is being accomplished according to plan.

Or very nearly so.

Mr. Neary, I'm told that we can count on your complete cooperation. What's your blood type?

I don't have the slightest idea.

Date of birth?

Uh...
December
4, 1944.

The last in line, Neary is met
by the little aliens who,
welcoming, gently take his
arms and lead him up the ramp.

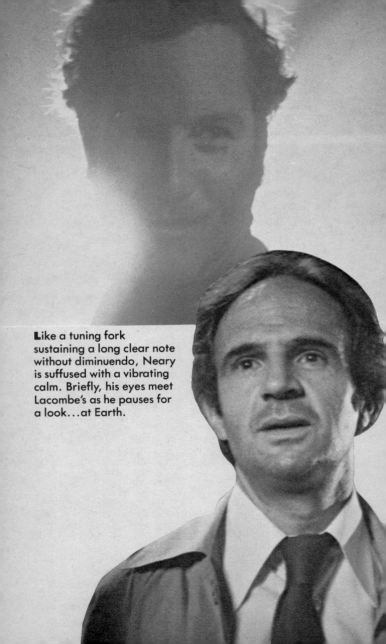

Like a tuning fork sustaining a long clear note without diminuendo, Neary is suffused with a vibrating calm. Briefly, his eyes meet Lacombe's as he pauses for a look...at Earth.

Then, turning, he disappears into brilliance.

Only one alien remains, the last to embark. Looking into the unearthly eyes, Lacombe finds assurance.

His hand is steady as he translates
the five-tone sequence, using the
signals developed by Zoltan
Kodaly.

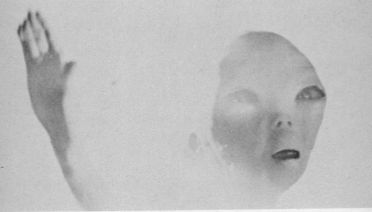

The alien responds,
repeating Lacombe's
gestures with a halting
stateliness.

The significance of the "person-to-person" communication sinks in on the crowd. And Lacombe, joyous, has to smile.

Watching Lacombe, an expression, perhaps universal, comes into the alien's face, mellowing the features.

Then, with simple dignity, the extraterrestrial turns and enters the ship.

The earth shakes as the massive spacecraft gets under way with a thunderous roaring, as if the very fabric of physics were stretched and vibrating.

With an easy grace the great vessel lifts starward, a celebration of light and energy.

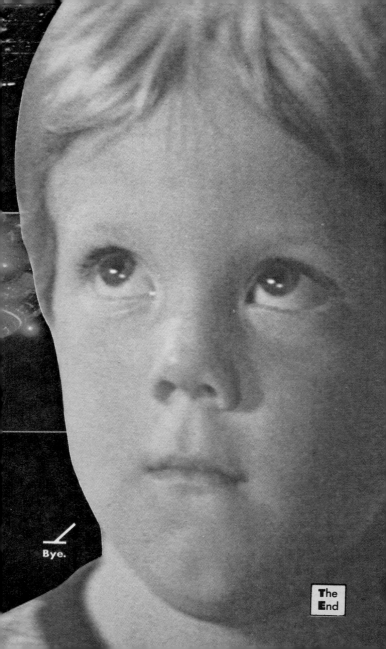

Bye.

The
End

Steven Spielberg, the movie's youthful writer and director, is known and respected as a man of multiple creative talents, boundless energy and an ability to accomplish the seemingly impossible on film.

This page Top: Spielberg discussing a scene with Dreyfuss (Roy Neary). **Bottom:** Spielberg settling a difference of opinion with Cary Guffey (Barry Guiler). Spielberg lost. **Opposite page:** Between scenes, Spielberg grabs a few moments of rest while talking to Justin Dreyfuss (Toby Neary).

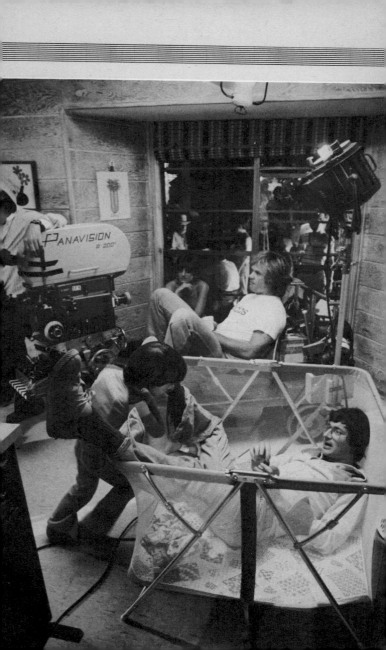

Opposite page: The camera moves in close to catch all the emotions of Melinda Dillon (Jillian Guiler) and Cary Guffey (Barry). **This page Top:** Douglas Slocombe, director of photography of the India sequence, sets up his next shot. **Bottom:** Cary Guffey